MESSAGE FROM DR. GÉZA SZILVAY
Head of the East Helsinki Music Institute and compiler of the
"Singing Rascals" series

Many today have all the material things they need: clothes, food, toys, etc. sometimes they have more than enough. Material things however cannot replace the warmth affection and time we give to the child, which is so important for its spiritual nourishment.

The "Singing Rascals" books are intended as a means of helping parents, grandparents, kindergarten and nursery school teachers, and all those who have children in their care, to create stimulating and purposeful moments with them.

The pictures, melodies and words in these books have been carefully chosen and arranged with young pre-school children in mind. The tunes have been selected from those which over the years have proved appealing and easy to learn, and are skilfully illustrated. The characters may be used to make up tales arising from the songs. The printed notation is only for the use of the adults.

The songs progress from two notes up to five notes (pentatonic) or seven notes (diatonic). Although for the sake of clarity they are written in C major and A minor, singing them in different keys, i.e. from different starting notes, is to be encouraged, thus suiting the children's own pitch registers. The use of solfa marking (Do-Re) makes it easy for parents to learn basic solmisation while children enjoy learning the pitch names and hand signs.

The series is supported by a parallel series of CDs on which infants sing and young children perform the melodies, but no CD, however good, can replace the lap and guidance of the close relative or friend.

The creation of Colourstrings Music Kindergartens is a significant step forward in the music education of the very young, and one in which I feel proud to play a part. My wish for all the little members is – joyous singing!

TO MY YOUNGEST SON

SINGING RASCALS LA
Original Finnish title LAULUVIIKARIN LA

This series of books is based on the teaching approach developed by
Géza Szilvay and is part of the instructional material
used by the Colourstrings Music Kindergartens.

The melodies in the SINGING RASCALS series reappear in the Colourstrings/
Colourkeys instrumental beginners books. Pupils find this
very helpful during the early stages of learning an instrument.

For further details of Colourstrings Music Kindergartens and teacher training,
visit our website:www.colourstrings.co.uk

This edition with grateful thanks to Pat, Andy and Verity Wislocki, Robin &
Lorna Ailes, Angela Edwards and George Saad.

Published by Colourstrings International Limited.
www.colourstringsbooks.com

ISBN – 978-1-873604-13-7
ISMN – 979-0-708023-06-7

SINGING RASCALS LA

Géza Szilvay

Illustrations: **Tuulia Hyrske**   Words: **Angela Ailes**

SONGS:

SWALLOWS IN THE SUNSHINE

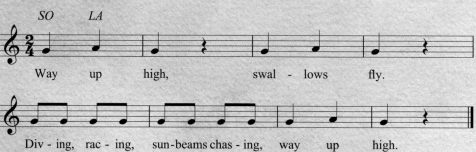

Way up high, swal - lows fly.

Div - ing, rac - ing, sun-beams chas - ing, way up high.

LA
SO

SAILING

SO   *LA*   *MI*

We are sail - ing can you see? Just us three.

Sail - ing far a - cross the sea, just us three.

2. We are sailing in our boat, jolly boat.
   Can you see us all afloat, we're afloat.

3. Sailing over waters blue, very blue.
   See us waving we're the crew, merry crew.

4. We are sailing on the seas, stormy seas.
   We are waiting for a breeze, little breeze.

5. We are sailing far from shore, distant shore.
   And we've never sailed before, not before.

6. As we're sailing seagulls cry, loud they cry.
   They are sailing in the sky, high blue sky.

7. We are sailing just us three, wet and free.
   Now we're sailing home to tea, just us three.

LA
SO

MI

THE WICKED MAGPIE

2. He's a very wicked magpie.
   In his shiny coat of black and white and blue.
   One day we will catch him, one day we will catch him.
   Then we'll send him straight off to the zoo.

LA
SO

MI

DO

TRUMPET

SO MI DO   LA   RE

I keep blow - ing, see me puff, see me pout.

Naugh - ty trum - pet, not a note will come out.

LA
SO

MI
RE DO

MISTER GOAT

Mis - ter Goat   I   beg your par - don,   but you're eat - ing   all our gar - den.

Mis - ter Goat   Sir,   it's a   scan - dal,   you're a   van - dal.
Mis - ter Goat   Sir,   what a   sil - ly,   gree - dy   bil - ly.

2. Mister Goat your bell is swinging, now we'll catch you when it's ringing.
    Mister Goat Sir, while you're lunching, flowers munching.
    Mister Goat you know we really, love you dearly.

10

LA SO
MI RE
DO
LA

FRANCIS DRAKE

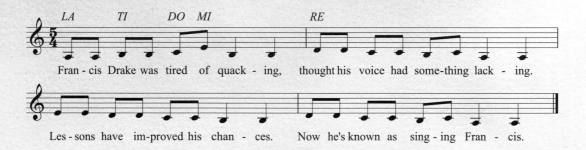

Fran - cis Drake was tired of quack - ing, thought his voice had some-thing lack - ing.

Les - sons have im-proved his chan - ces. Now he's known as sing - ing Fran - cis.

2. Francis went to violin land. Married Dinah Duck from Finland.
   Happily her eggs she's laying, while the kantele he's playing.

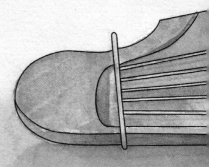

MI
RE
DO
TI
LA

HUSH LITTLE BABY

LA — MI — FA — RE

Soft through the win - dow night - time is creep - ing.

DO — TI

Hush lit - tle ba - by, now's time for sleep - ing.

2. Birds are not singing bees are not humming.
   Hush little baby dreamland is coming.

FA
MI
RE
DO
TI
LA

SLEEPY BEAR

From the trees the leaves fall quick - ly, cov - er - ing the ground so thick - ly.

Slee - py bear it is not play - time, win - ter's here it's hide - a - way time.

LA
SO
FA
MI
RE
DO
TI
LA

LA

TI

DO

RE

MI

FA
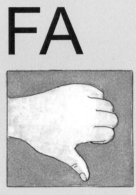

SO

LA
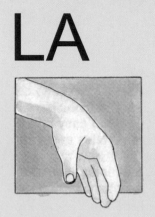

Singing Rascals Series

Books

Audio CDs

Exercise Books

Tunes used in this book are based on traditional children's and folk melodies.

Mister Goat, composed by Pál Járdányi

Trumpet composed by Zoltán Kodály © 1962 by Zoltán Kodály, New edition © 1970 by Boosey & Hawkes Music Publishers Ltd.

Rhythm Rascals Series

Books

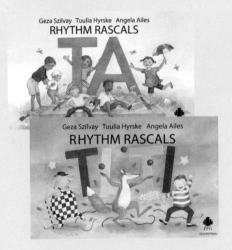

Audio CDs

Exercise Books